'Nice Bear, Naughty Bear'
is an original concept by
© Diana Mather, Avril Lethbridge
& Mary-Ann Mackenzie.

Author Copyright © Diana Mather,
Avril Lethbridge
& Mary-Ann Mackenzie.

Illustrated by Mary-Ann Mackenzie

Maverick Arts Publishing Ltd
Studio 4 Hardham Mill Park
Hardham Pulborough
West Sussex RH20 1LA
+44 (0) 179887 5980

© Maverick Arts Publishing Limited (2010)

PUBLISHED BY MAVERICK ARTS
PUBLISHING LTD

ISBN 978-1-84886-039-1

Maverick

www.maverickartsclub.com

Nice Bear Naughty Bear

THE GOOD MANNERS BOOK

NICE BEARS
NAUGHTY BEARS

There are nice bears and naughty bears
Shy bears and haughty bears

Messy bears, oh what a sight
And bears that always think they're right

Bully bears that have no friends
And kind bears that make amends

Pushing, shoving, grumpy bears
Not bothering to see who cares

But you and I know bears that say
Please and thank you every day

And soon all bears are bound to find
Life is nicer when you are kind.

Rude Bear

Feeling angry, feeling mad

Try not to make others sad

There's no excuse for being rude

Just because you're in a mood

Please Bear

Please is such a magic word

Make certain that it's always heard

Please remember, don't forget

And you will be the best bear yet

Moaning Bear

Moaning bear says "Nothing's fair
I'll do as I like, I don't care"

Little bears who often moan
Will soon find that they play alone

Helpful Bear

Helpful bears will always ask

If they can help with any task

If you are a helpful bear

You'll be welcome everywhere

Greedy Bear

Greedy bears take more than they need
And then eat it with disgusting speed

Those bears who take and take
Might end up with tummy ache

Sharing Bear

Sharing Bear says "Join the fun!

Work and play with everyone"

Sharing makes for happy bears

As it shows that someone cares

Bully Bear

Bears who fight and spoil a game
Will not be asked to play again

A bully bear is no one's friend
And will be lonely in the end

Kind Bear

Bears who are always kind

Make good friends, you will find

If they are there when things go wrong

You won't be sad for very long

Nose Picker Bear

It really is an ugly pose
To stick your fingers up your nose

No bear wants to look at you
They have better things to do

Table Manners Bear

Sit up straight and don't be late

Eat the food that's on your plate

Keep your mouth shut when you chew

That's the proper thing to do

Boasting Bear

Showing off is never clever

Smart bears don't do it ..... EVER!

Boasting comes before a fall

Not a good idea at all

Thank you Bear

Thank you takes no time to say
But it can help in every way

Polite bears are bound to find
That life is nicer when you're kind

Yelling Bear

Yelling is a horrid noise

That never gets you treats or toys

Making a terrible hullabaloo

Is something better not to do

Sorry Bear

If you do something wrong,

Saying sorry won't take long.

It's such a simple word to say

Making things right in every way

'There are nice bears and naughty bears
Happy bears and sad bears

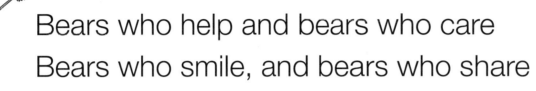

Bears who help and bears who care
Bears who smile, and bears who share

Soon all bears are bound to find
That 'manners' are just being kind

Then mummies, daddies, everyone
Will say to their bears, WELL DONE '